1001
Things to Find

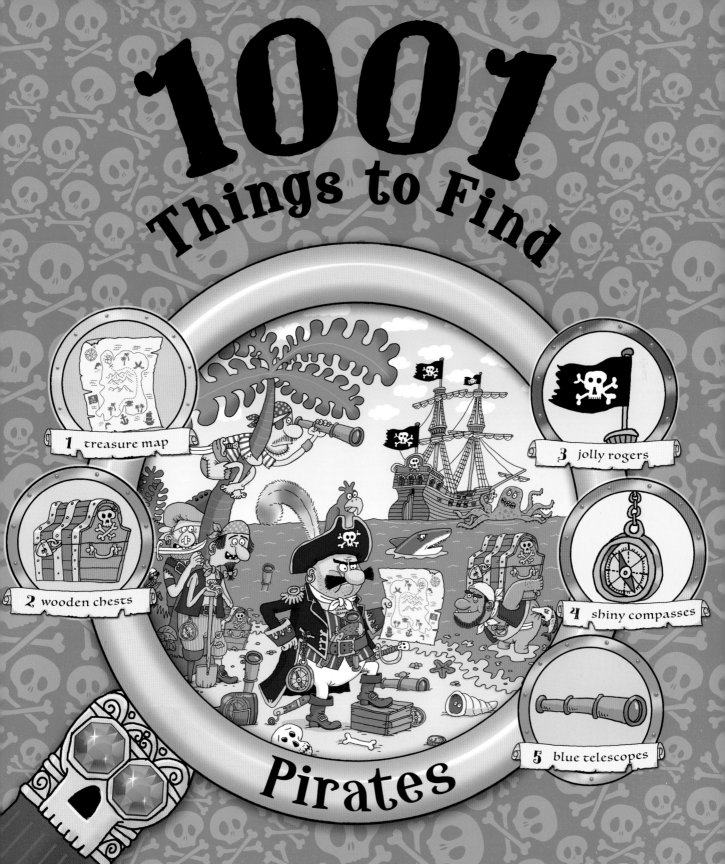

1 treasure map

2 wooden chests

3 jolly rogers

4 shiny compasses

5 blue telescopes

Pirates

igloobooks

Can you find 1001 pirate things?

Ahoy there, mateys! Captain Nobeard and his first mate, Fearless Fiona, are sailing the seven seas in search of hidden treasure. Many years ago, the notorious Hookhand Hamish buried his gold, tore up the treasure map and scattered the pieces on the ocean winds. Now it's down to Captain Nobeard and his crew to find all the pieces to discover the hoard.

In every swashbuckling scene you'll need to find Captain Nobeard, Fearless Fiona and a piece of the treasure map. There are lots of other interesting items to spot on the voyage, too, but first it's time to get The Grizzly Sinker shipshape before it can set sail.

Captain Nobeard

Fearless Fiona

A piece of the treasure map

Let's have a practice first. On the opposite page, see if you can spot Captain Nobeard, Fearless Fiona and a piece of the map. Once you've found them, see if you can spot the items below, too.

6 pairs of
rubber gloves

14 feather
dusters

18 red
mops

At the Docks

Y'arr! A golden sun rises over the sea as the bandits stock The Grizzly Sinker with supplies for their voyage. Can you spot Captain Nobeard, Fearless Fiona and a piece of the map?

3 silver banjos

4 peg legs

5 pirate flags

6 clucking chickens

7 heavy cannons

8 heavy cannonballs

9 green telescopes

10 swashbuckling swords

12 mischievous mice

13 hungry seagulls

All Aboard

Yo-ho-ho! The sea is calm and it's almost time to set sail. Who knows what the crooked crew will encounter. Can you find Captain Nobeard, Fearless Fiona and a piece of the map?

3 dull anchors

4 chef hats

5 teddy bears

6 important scrolls

7 stripy fish

8 scary spiders

9 copper tankards

10 red ladles

12 grizzly bones

15 revolting rats

Desert Island

Why did the crab cross the island? To get to the other tide!
The sun's out so the pirates have stopped off for some beach fun.
Find Captain Nobeard, Fearless Fiona and a piece of the map.

3 stripy
parasols

6 chocolate
ice creams

9 fruity
drinks

10 angry
crabs

15 pink
spades

Enemy Ahead

There's a rival ship in the distance! Luckily, Fearless Fiona is there to save the day and prepares the lawless gang for battle. Find Captain Nobeard, Fearless Fiona and a piece of the map.

3 bottles of ginger beer

6 swinging lanterns

9 wooden barrels

10 water balloons

15 super slingshots

Cutlass Crew

The Grizzly Sinker gang is putting up a good fight against the rival plundering pirates. Even the cat and dog are scrapping. Spot Captain Nobeard, Fearless Fiona and a piece of the map.

3 golden padlocks

4 rope ladders

5 bunches of keys

6 shark fins

7 stripy lifebelts

8 rainbow feathers

9 pouches of money

10 blocks of gold

12 poisonous jellyfish

15 rotten tomatoes

Super Storm

It's all hands on deck! A bone-rattling storm crashes into the ship. Will The Grizzly Sinker live up to its name? Spot Captain Nobeard, Fearless Fiona and a piece of the map.

3 rowing boats

4 pirate buckets

5 bolts of lightning

6 stripy umbrellas

7 terrified turtles

8 harpoon forks

9 yellow sandbags

10 sharp fish bones

12 angry piranhas

15 red goggles

Grub Galore

The brave buccaneers survive the storm and it's time to celebrate. There's foul fish-eye stew and octopus soup for all. Can you spot Captain Nobeard, Fearless Fiona and a piece of the map?

3 pans of octopus soup

6 chicken drumsticks

9 shiny candelabra

10 blocks of mouldy cheese

15 skull forks

Under the Sea

The Grizzly Sinker crew dives into the ocean and discovers an old pirate ship that has met a watery end. Can you find Captain Nobeard, Fearless Fiona and a piece of the map?

3 friendly dolphins

6 angry angler fish

9 pieces of coral

10 stripy sea snails

15 pink clamshells

Monster Madness

What do sea monsters eat? Fish and ships! A very peckish giant squid is hungry for pirates. Can you find Captain Nobeard, Fearless Fiona and a piece of the map?

3 spiky cactus

4 fish heads

5 scuttling beetles

6 bent spoons

7 mouldy mushrooms

8 buzzing flies

9 rowing oars

10 blue bows

12 silver cutlasses

15 sharp arrows

Land Ahoy!

The pirates head ashore, but there's no stopping for ice cream at this beach. There's treasure to find and they're getting closer. Find Captain Nobeard, Fearless Fiona and a piece of the map.

3 stripy surfboards

6 rubber dinghies

9 spiky pineapples

10 nosy toucans

15 yellow sunglasses

Wild Jungle

The crew ventures through the deadly jungle in hope of finding the treasure, but there are some very hungry tigers on the loose. Spot Captain Nobeard, Fearless Fiona and the last bit of the map.

3 grumpy tigers

6 yellow bananas

9 cheeky monkeys

10 poisonous apples

15 deadly, spotted bugs

Treasure Cove

Yo-ho-ho! The treasure map is complete and the crew has hit the jackpot! There are gold doubloons for all. Can you spot Captain Nobeard and Fearless Fiona?

3 gold
statues

4 precious
globes

5 treasure
chests

6 armour
helmets

7 heart-shaped
necklaces

8 fire
torches

9 ruby
rings

10 swooping
bats

12 sparkly
crowns

15 ropes
of pearls

Pirate Party

Y'arr! There's a beach celebration for the whole crew
and the plundering pirates party until the sun goes down.
Spot Captain Nobeard and Fearless Fiona enjoying the party.

3 happy
giraffes

4 clumsy
elephants

5 stripy
party hats

6 boxes of
popcorn

7 jugs of
fizzy pop

8 pink
accordions

9 sleepy
hermit crabs

10 rainbow
lollipops

12 pirate
balloons

15 pieces
of cake

Good work, me hearties! You've helped Captain Nobeard and
Fearless Fiona find the lost treasure. Now go back and see if you can
find each of these cool characters and items in every scene, too.

Ruby-encrusted
cutlass

Captain
Claws

A rare
parrot

A precious
skull goblet

A golden
compass

Gary the
ghost pirate

A hook
hand

A message
in a bottle

How closely were you looking at each scene? Go back and see if
you can spot which scene each of these items was hidden in.

A rather
peckish snake

A mermaid
taking a bath

A pirate
learning to read

A pesky dog
stealing sausages